The Cancer Prayer Journal

for Women

This Journal Belongs to:

Copyright@2022 Sandy Popp
All rights reserved
ISBN:9798356622229
Lion Hearts Press

From My Heart to Yours

"Help, God" is a prayer; we don't need to be eloquent or even use words with Him. Journaling and strategically focusing my prayers positively impacted my 2014 Stage 4 Breast Cancer journey. Recording the real, raw, honest, and desperate moments is powerful, if not necessary at this time. This private journal will one day be a compelling reminder of how you fought this and how a loving, faithful, and mighty God walked with you during one of the darkest parts of your life. I pray that within the difficulties, God will show you His grace, faithfulness, and love in a new and unique way. You have my heartfelt love and earnest prayers for your journey. You aren't alone, the Lord fights for you.

Contents

My Year of Prayer

JANUARY

FEBRUARY

MARCH

APRIL

MAY

JUNE

JULY

AUGUST

SEPTEMBER

OCTOBER

NOVEMBER

DECEMBER

Lay your hand on this calendar and pray that God blesses each appointment, decision, event, or treatment toward your healing, health, and restoration. I'm praying for your year too.

The Diagnosis

My Name: _____

My Oncologist: _____

Date: _____

The Diagnosis: _____

_____

_____

_____

My Healing Goals: *We are more than a physical body. My goals*

touched on the physical, mental, emotional, social, and spiritual.

_____

_____

_____

_____

_____

_____

_____

_____

_____

"Fear not, for I am with you; be not dismayed, for I am
your God; I will strengthen you, I will help you, I will
uphold you with my righteous right hand." Isaiah 41:10

Scripture Based Prayers

It's powerful to apply scriptures personally. Below are a few prayers and their corresponding scriptures. Scriptures will come to your mind as they do; write them and your prayers below.

Scripture	Scripture-based Personal Prayers
Matthew 28:20	Thank you, God, that you will be with me each step of my entire cancer journey.
Psalm 34:18	You are the closest when I'm hurting the worst; help me to feel it and know it.

The Bible isn't a regular book. It's spiritual and a powerful resource for our cancer journey. Hebrews 4:12

My Prayer Team

Ask those who love you and those who pray regularly to be on your Cancer Prayer team. I communicated with my team through a private online group. Post pictures of your prayer request pages from this journal to save time. It's a quick way to keep everyone informed and praying in agreement.

Name:

Phone:

Name:

Phone:

Name:

Phone:

Name:

Phone:

Name:

Phone:

Name:

Phone:

God visits us when even two or three agree together in prayer. Miracles happen when he comes. Matt.8:19-20

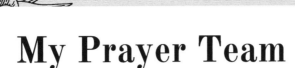

My Prayer Team

Name:

Phone:

Name:

Phone:

Name:

Phone:

Name:

Phone:

Name:

Phone:

Name:

Phone:

Name:

Phone:

James 5:15 says the prayer of faith will save the one who's sick. There are people with a calling of prayer. Find them and get them on your team.

My Medical Team

Name: **Phone:**

Address:

Specialty:

Notes/Prayer:

Name: **Phone:**

Address:

Specialty:

Notes/Prayer:

Name: **Phone:**

Address:

Specialty:

Notes/Prayer:

Name: **Phone:**

Address:

Specialty:

Notes/Prayer:

Lord, guide the hearts and minds of this medical team to align with your perfect will for my sister's healing. Pr. 21:1

 # My Medical Team

Name: **Phone:**
Address:
Specialty:
Notes/Prayer:

Name: **Phone:**
Address:
Specialty:
Notes/Prayer:

Name: **Phone:**
Address:
Specialty:
Notes/Prayer:

Name: **Phone:**
Address:
Specialty:
Notes/Prayer:

Everyone thinks they'll remember important questions for their doctor, but no one does. Discuss with loved ones, write out questions for the doctor ahead of time, and record the answers. (There's space in "Medical Appointments")

Medical Appointments

Doctor		Date	
Address		Speciality	
Purpose			
My Questions			
Answers			
Goal			

Doctor		Date	
Address		Speciality	
Purpose			
My Questions			
Answers			
Goal			

Medical Appointments

Doctor		Date	
Address		Speciality	
Purpose			
My Questions			
Answers			
Goal			

Doctor		Date	
Address		Speciality	
Purpose			
My Questions			
Answers			
Goal			

 Medical Appointments

Doctor		Date	
Address		Speciality	
Purpose			
My Questions			
Answers			
Goal			

Doctor		Date	
Address		Speciality	
Purpose			
My Questions			
Answers			
Goal			

Medical Appointments

Doctor		Date	
Address		Speciality	
Purpose			
My Questions			
Answers			
Goal			

Doctor		Date	
Address		Speciality	
Purpose			
My Questions			
Answers			
Goal			

Medical Appointments

Doctor		Date	
Address		Speciality	
Purpose			
My Questions			
Answers			
Goal			

Doctor		Date	
Address		Speciality	
Purpose			
My Questions			
Answers			
Goal			

Medical Appointments

Doctor		Date	
Address		Speciality	
Purpose			
My Questions			
Answers			
Goal			

Doctor		Date	
Address		Speciality	
Purpose			
My Questions			
Answers			
Goal			

Prayer for Treatments, Scans, & Results

Date: _____ Appointment Type: _____

Location: _____

Prayer Request :*(i.e. symptoms, nausea, pain, anxiety, fear, finances)*

_____

_____

_____

_____

I'm Grateful For: _____

_____

Date: _____ Appointment Type: _____

Location: _____

Prayer Request :*(i.e. symptoms, nausea, pain, anxiety, fear, finances)*

_____

_____

_____

I'm Grateful For: _____

_____

"The Lord will fight for you."
Exodus 14:14 NIV

Prayer for Treatments, Scans, & Results

Date: _____ **Appointment Type:** _____

Location: _____

Prayer Request :_(i.e. symptoms, nausea, pain, anxiety, fear, finances)_

_____

_____

_____

I'm Grateful For:

_____

_____

Date: _____ **Appointment Type:** _____

Location: _____

Prayer Request :_(i.e. symptoms, nausea, pain, anxiety, fear, finances)_

_____

_____

_____

I'm Grateful For:

_____

_____

The Holy Spirit helps us to pray for God's perfect will. Ro. 8:26-27

Prayer for Treatments, Scans, & Results

Date: _____ Appointment Type: _____

Location: _____

Prayer Request :*(i.e. symptoms, nausea, pain, anxiety, fear, finances)*

_____

_____

_____

_____

I'm Grateful For: _____

_____

Date: _____ Appointment Type: _____

Location: _____

Prayer Request :*(i.e. symptoms, nausea, pain, anxiety, fear, finances)*

_____

_____

_____

_____

I'm Grateful For: _____

_____

Faith can move mountains.
Mark 11:22-24

Prayer for Treatments, Scans, & Results

Date: _____ **Appointment Type:** _____

Location: _____

Prayer Request : *(i.e. symptoms, nausea, pain, anxiety, fear, finances)*

_____

_____

_____

_____

I'm Grateful For: _____

_____

Date: _____ **Appointment Type:** _____

Location: _____

Prayer Request : *(i.e. symptoms, nausea, pain, anxiety, fear, finances)*

_____

_____

_____

_____

I'm Grateful For: _____

_____

"Fear not..." Is.41:10

Prayer for Treatments, Scans, & Results

Date: _____ Appointment Type: _____

Location: _____

Prayer Request : *(i.e. symptoms, nausea, pain, anxiety, fear, finances)*

_____

_____

_____

_____

I'm Grateful For: _____

_____

_____

Date: _____ Appointment Type: _____

Location: _____

Prayer Request : *(i.e. symptoms, nausea, pain, anxiety, fear, finances)*

_____

_____

_____

I'm Grateful For: _____

_____

_____

Seek, ask, and knock.
Luke 11:9-13

Prayer for Treatments, Scans, & Results

Date: _____ **Appointment Type:** _____

Location: _____

Prayer Request :*(i.e. symptoms, nausea, pain, anxiety, fear, finances)*

_____

_____

_____

_____

I'm Grateful For: _____

_____

Date: _____ **Appointment Type:** _____

Location: _____

Prayer Request :*(i.e. symptoms, nausea, pain, anxiety, fear, finances)*

_____

_____

_____

_____

I'm Grateful For: _____

_____

There is power in the agreement in prayer. Matt.18:19-20

Prayer for Treatments, Scans, & Results

Date: _____ **Appointment Type:** _____

Location: _____

Prayer Request :_(i.e. symptoms, nausea, pain, anxiety, fear, finances)_

_____

_____

_____

_____

I'm Grateful For: _____

_____

Date: _____ **Appointment Type:** _____

Location: _____

Prayer Request :_(i.e. symptoms, nausea, pain, anxiety, fear, finances)_

_____

_____

_____

I'm Grateful For: _____

_God hears us when we pray in
Jesus' name. John 14:13_

Prayer for Treatments, Scans, & Results

Date: _____ Appointment Type: _____

Location: _____

Prayer Request :*(i.e. symptoms, nausea, pain, anxiety, fear, finances)*

_____

_____

_____

_____

I'm Grateful For: _____

Date: _____ Appointment Type: _____

Location: _____

Prayer Request :*(i.e. symptoms, nausea, pain, anxiety, fear, finances)*

_____

_____

_____

I'm Grateful For: _____

God can do more than we can think, ask or imagine. Ephesians 3:20

Prayer for Treatments, Scans, & Results

Date: _____ Appointment Type: _____

Location: _____

Prayer Request :*(i.e. symptoms, nausea, pain, anxiety, fear, finances)*

_____

_____

_____

_____

I'm Grateful For: _____

_____

Date: _____ Appointment Type: _____

Location: _____

Prayer Request :*(i.e. symptoms, nausea, pain, anxiety, fear, finances)*

_____

_____

_____

_____

I'm Grateful For: _____

_____

"He will call upon Me, and I will answer him; I will be with him in trouble; I will rescue him and honor him. With long life, I will satisfy him, and show him my salvation." Ps.91:15-16

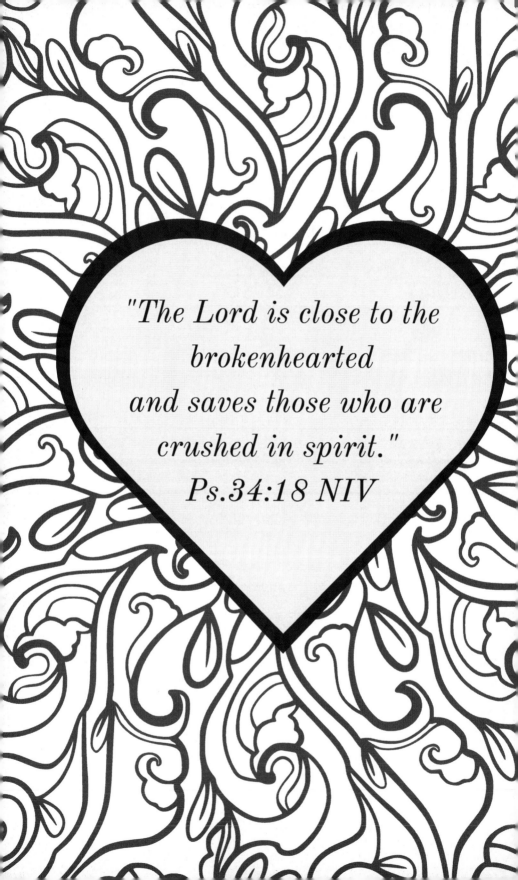

"The Lord is close to the
brokenhearted
and saves those who are
crushed in spirit."
Ps.34:18 NIV

My Prayer Requests

Prayer Needs: **Date:**

_____
_____
_____
_____
_____
_____
_____
_____

Prayer Needs   **Date:**

_____
_____
_____
_____
_____
_____
_____

God gives us peace in every way and
all the time. 2 Thessalonians 3:16

My Prayer Requests

Prayer Needs: **Date:**

Prayer Needs   **Date:**

Jesus prays for us. Romans 8:34

My Prayer Requests

Prayer Needs: **Date:**

Prayer Needs   **Date:**

"All things are possible with God."
Mark 10:27

My Prayer Requests

Prayer Needs: **Date:**

Prayer Needs   **Date:**

Prayer of faith saves the sick.
James 5:14-15

My Prayer Requests

Prayer Needs: **Date:**

_____

_____

_____

_____

_____

_____

_____

_____

Prayer Needs   **Date:**

_____

_____

_____

_____

_____

_____

_____

_____

He restores our health and
life. Isaiah 38:16

My Prayer Requests

Prayer Needs: **Date:**

_____

_____

_____

_____

_____

_____

_____

_____

Prayer Needs   **Date:**

_____

_____

_____

_____

_____

_____

_____

God listens to our prayers.

Psalm 66:19

My Prayer Requests

Prayer Needs: **Date:**

Prayer Needs   **Date:**

God can heal and replace what cancer
steals and destroys. Psalms 107:2

My Prayer Requests

Prayer Needs: **Date:**

_____

_____

_____

_____

_____

_____

_____

_____

Prayer Needs   **Date:**

_____

_____

_____

_____

_____

_____

_____

_____

_____

Nothing is too hard for God.
Jeremiah 32:27

My Prayer Requests

Prayer Needs: Date:

Prayer Needs   Date:

The impassioned and effectual prayers of
God's people can work miracles. Jas.5:1

My Prayer Requests

Prayer Needs: **Date:**

Prayer Needs   **Date:**

Thank you, Jesus, that we can find our healing within the wounds you suffered. 1 Pet.2:24

Heart Storms

Date:

"Heart Storm" pages are for much-needed unguarded moments in the cancer walk. You can draw, doodle, and scribble; these pages have no rules. God didn't create us to bury these feelings, and with cancer, we can't. Let the storm rage on the page. God meets us powerfully in our places of honesty.

Heart Storms

God can handle our negative feelings. He knows them all anyhow.

Heart Storms

Date:

The depth of our honesty becomes the depth of our liberty. Jesus said in John 8:32 that the truth sets us free.

Heart Storms

Sometimes, we need to stop denying our feelings in the name of faith or strength and let it flow and then let it go.

! Journal

Chemo #1   Monday

I am scared & anxious.
The unknown of the chemo journey
is A LoT.

Day 1   Tuesday
exhausted + constantly queasy
Day 2   Wednesday
- got a walk in with my friend Jen. It
felt good to get out + do something
- by tonight I feel miserable. Meds must be
wearing off. Everything hurts, every noise hurts my
head to my bones. feeling worthless
Day 3 Thursday
- traveling to San Diego for Millie's winter
break. I am feeling like death but mind
over matter. This will be worth it!
Day 4 Friday
Glad to have a down day at the hotel
by myself to recover. Lisa, Cory + kids
went to Lego Land.

Even though I walk through the valley of cancer, I don't need to
fear because God is with me. Psalms 23:4

Day 5 Saturday
- I am on the upswing. Went on a Harbor Cruise, then nap for Augie + myself then Sea World from 3:30 - 8:00.
It was a great day!
Day 6 Sunday
~ Cory, kids + Lisa took a trolley ride to Corando Island. I met them with the rental car. Kids played on the beach. It was a cool 60° but they loved playing in the sand. Lisa, Augie + I came back for quiet time. Cory & Miller went to the pool. BRRRR.
- Cory + I met up with neighbors Coli + David for some dinner + drinks It felt great to be out of "normal" engagement
Day 6 ~~Sunday~~ Monday
~ San Diego Zoo

✒ Journal

God watches over me in all things. Every appointment, scan, and treatment, He is there. I place the results in His hands. Ps.121:8

Chemo #2 Monday
- Going solo to chemo. It is such
a marathon of a day 6hrs ish
from lab draw to chemo infusion complete
- I'm Dreading the drive but staying
focused on "get it done".

Day 1 Tuesday
- I seem to be figuring out the
sluggish tummy + queasy is better too
- I slept most the day away but
didn't "feel bad"

Day 2 Wednesday
Weather is cold + gross - this does not
motivate me for a walk
I took a shower. I cried. Clumps +
handfuls of hair are coming out. It is
alarming + so upsetting. No more hiding.

God sees where and how this cancer is attacking my body and
knows how to heal it. Ps. 139:12

Journal

You may not be able to handle cancer, but God can. Keep putting it in his hands. ♡*Sandy*

 # Journal

Date

Today I'm grateful for...

📝 Journal

God hears me when I pray. Ps, 34:15

♪ Journal

God leads me on the pathway of life. Ps. 16:11

God Treasures You

"Are not two sparrows sold for a penny? Yet not one of them will fall to the ground outside your Father's care. So don't be afraid; you are worth more than many sparrows." Matthew 10:29 & 31

✒ Journal

Date

There is no courage without fear to face. When you're scared,
you're much more courageous than you feel.♡ Sandy

✒ Journal

Date

I can lie down and sleep peacefully because God is with me. Ps. 4:8

Journal

Today I'm grateful for...

Journal

5-Minute Journal Prompt

In what ways does your body tell you it's tired and you need to stop and rest? What are some techniques you can use to get your body the extra rest it needs?

Journal

God can lead you through it. He did it for me; he can do it for you.
♡*Sandy*

✒ Journal

God helps me with every anxious thought. Phil.4:6-7

 # Journal

Today I'm grateful for...

Mental Health Check-in

How I'm feeling today

Date _____

What is your biggest worry today? _____

_____

_____

_____

_____

_____

Does anything help ease your concern? If so, what? _____

_____

_____

_____

_____

When I cry to God, he hears & delivers me.
Ps 34:4

Is this something I should

mention to my cancer

counselor or therapist?

Yes, No, Maybe

Journal

The practice of gratefulness is a mighty tool for a cancer patient.
It's a practical way to implement Romans 12:21. ♡*Sandy*

✒ Journal

Today I'm grateful for...

Journal

There are some answers we won't know this side of heaven. Don't allow that to discourage you, just keep moving forward.
♡ _Sandy_

Journal

My heart will not be troubled because You are with me. John 14:27

Journal

*Everyone is dealing with their own pain & fear from this
cancer. Not one person handles this perfectly.* ♡*Sandy*

✦ Journal

Date

We get strength from joy. Nehemiah 8:10

Restorative Bingo

Catch up with Friends	Take a Long Shower or Bath	Have Fun	Spend Time in Praise & Worship
Watch or Do Something to Make me Laugh	Give Myself Grace	Take A Social Media Break	Get 8 Hours Of Sleep
Spend Time In Nature	Rest or Nap if I'm Tired	Take a Walk	Work on Boundaries
Snuggle Up & Read	Hug a pet or Loved One	Move My Body Joyfully to Music	Practice a Coping Skill

✒ Journal

Date

Don't work yourself to death right now. You're fighting for your
life. It's okay for people to discover that you're human♡Sandy

 # Journal

5-Minute Journal Prompt

In 2 Corinthians 12:10, the Apostle Paul didn't despise his weaknesses but embraced them because that's where he saw God's power. In what ways is this relevant or encouraging for cancer patients?

✒ Journal

I am courageous because God is for me. Romans 8:31

 # Journal

Today I'm grateful for...

Mental Health Check-in

How I'm feeling today

Date _____

List some prominent emotions that you've noticed over the last couple of weeks.

_____

_____

_____

_____

_____

Can you list specific events that may feed or trigger them?

_____

_____

_____

_____

_____

God knows our thoughts and triggers.
Ps. 139:2

Is this something I should mention to my cancer counselor or therapist?

Yes, No, Maybe

✒ Journal

Sometimes it's hard to have faith and easy to doubt. If you don't know where to start, try doubting your doubts. ♡ _Sandy_

✒ Journal

If we need more faith in an area, the key is in Romans 10:14,17.
Speak and meditate on God's word. It works. ♡ _Sandy_

 # Journal

5-Minute Journal Prompt

**What kinds of thoughts keep you awake at night?
What do you do to get back to sleep? Research
and write other techniques you can try to return
to sleep.**

Journal

In Mark 9:24, the father of a very sick child asked Jesus to help his unbelief. We can pray that same prayer.♡Sandy

# Journal

Date

Today I'm grateful for...

Journal

Cancer may bring us to our knees, but God will lovingly lift us up.
♡Sandy

Journal

God restores my health and gives me life. Is. 38:16

 Journal   *Date*

5-Minute Journal Prompt

A cancer playlist helped me through some difficult
times and emotional situations. As you discover songs
that make you feel empowered, worshipful, joyful,
courageous, peaceful, or happy, write them here and
play them often.

✒ Journal

God can heal and deliver me from anything that causes destruction in my life. Psalm 107:20

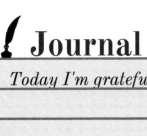

Journal

Today I'm grateful for...

✒ Journal

Cancer will not prosper in my body. Is. 54:7

✒ Journal

You are not a burden. ♡Sandy

Journal

When you have a choice, focus on the positive over the negative. If it's too difficult, get help. We can't do this alone. ♡*Sandy*

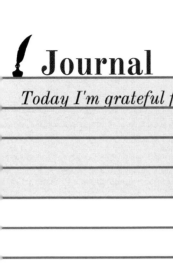
Journal

Date

Today I'm grateful for...

Mental Health Check-in

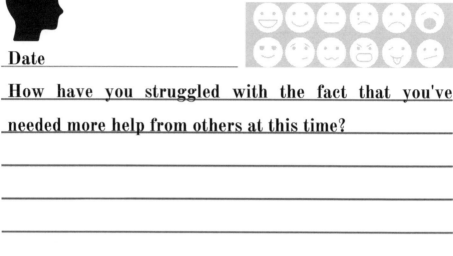

How I'm feeling today

Date _____

How have you struggled with the fact that you've
needed more help from others at this time?

_____

_____

_____

_____

Do you allow others to help you when you need it?
Why or why not? How does it make you feel when you
need extra help?

_____

_____

_____

_____

_____

God brings people to help in dark times. Pr. 17:17

Is this something I should
mention to my cancer
counselor or therapist?

Yes, No, Maybe

Journal

God designed us to need others. We can't to do it alone.

♡*Sandy*

 # Journal

5-Minute Journal Prompt

Jesus demonstrated the human need for others while carrying his cross. Simon of Cyrene came alongside him to help bear the weight. Who are or could be the Simons in your life?

Journal

I am loved. Romans 8:32

Journal

*Thank you, God, that when I keep my mind on you, I have your
perfect peace. Isaiah 26:3*

Journal

God goes in front of you, walks beside you, and
watches behind you. ♡Sandy

✒ Journal

I sometimes feel isolated or deserted in my pain, but take comfort in knowing that God will never leave me. Ps 27:10

Journal

Date

Today I'm grateful for...

Mental Health Check-in

Date _____

Most cancer patients experience the blow of a loved one dropping out of their lives during the treatment. Can you want to list them and how this affected you?

_____

_____

_____

_____

_____

_____

_____

_____

_____

_____

Even if my mom & dad leave me, God takes me in.
Ps. 27:10

Is this something I should mention to my cancer counselor or therapist?

Yes, No, Maybe

✒ Journal

God will never leave or abandon me. Hebrews 13:5

You are loved!

"I have loved you with an everlasting love."
Jeremiah 31:3

# Journal

Date

Today I'm grateful for...

 # Journal

5-Minute Journal Prompt

In what ways are boundaries needed during your cancer journey?

What new boundaries have you set (or need to set) to protect yourself as you are healing?

✒ Journal

Date

Cancer might bring some change to many relationships. Don't try
to protect people from the personal growth they need.♡Sandy

✒ Journal

_____
_____
_____
_____
_____
_____
_____
_____
_____
_____
_____
_____
_____
_____
_____
_____
_____
_____
_____
_____
_____
_____
_____
_____
_____

This may be one of the easiest times in your life to set boundaries.

♡*Sandy*

Journal

When I give my plans to God, He makes a clear path for me. Pr. 3:6

# Journal

Date

Today I'm grateful for...

Mental Health Check-in

How I'm feeling today

Date _____

Do you deal with guilt or negative self-talk? What are some of those thoughts?

_____

_____

_____

_____

At this time, we become more sensitive to unhealthy ways of thinking. Can you think of some strategies to battle these thoughts?

_____

_____

_____

We have no condemnation in Jesus. Rom. 8:1-15

Is this something I should mention to my cancer counselor or therapist?

Yes, No, Maybe

❦ Journal

Thank you, God, for new mercy every day. Lam. 3:22-23

Journal

God is my protector and helper in every part of this cancer journey.

Psalms 46:1

 # Journal

Date

Today I'm grateful for...

✒ Journal

Lord, I pray that this cancer formed against my sister will not get stronger, but will be defeated. In Jesus' name.   ♡Sandy

f Journal

God knows what we need even before we ask him. Mt. 6:8

Journal

Date

Today I'm grateful for...

Journal

Date

He's working behind the scenes, even when you don't feel Him.
♡*Sandy*

Journal

5-Minute Journal Prompt

Exodus 23:25 says that God will bless our food & drink
and deliver our bodies from sickness. How can you
apply this to the way you bless your food?

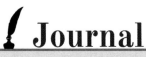 # Journal

Date

Today I'm grateful for...

Mental Health Check-in

How I'm feeling today

Date _____

Is there an instance (or three) where you had to be strong for others when you were weak? _____

_____

_____

_____

_____

What kinds of actions by others can make you feel cared for? _____

_____

_____

_____

_____

Though trouble surrounds me on all sides, my spirit sustains me. Pr. 18:14

Is this something I should mention to my cancer counselor or therapist?

Yes, No, Maybe

✒ Journal

Cancer can never separate me from God's love. Rom. 8:35-39

 # Journal

Date

5-Minute Journal Prompt

Proverbs 17:17 tells us that God brings people into our lives during times of trouble. In what ways have people shown up for you during this journey? I count strangers who hold open a door or offer a place in line.

✒ Journal

God can handle anything that comes my way. Jeremiah 32:17

Journal

Today I'm grateful for...

Journal

Lay it all at the foot of the cross and keep laying it down until it stays there. The more you do it, the easier it gets. ♡ *Sandy*

Journal

*God thinks about me with kindness in His heart. He wants me to
have hope and a good future. Jeremiah 33:11.*

# Journal

Today I'm grateful for...

✒ Journal

Date

He remembers my tears and forgets my sins. Ps. 56:8, 103:12

 # Journal

Date

Today I'm grateful for...

Mental Health Check-in

How I'm feeling today

Date _____

1 John 4:18 says that torment and fear are related. It also says that perfect love can conquer fear. What fear(s) torment you? _____

_____

_____

_____

Is it difficult for you to receive love in some areas? Why do you think that is?

_____

_____

_____

God is my hiding place and my refuge. Ps. 46:1

Is this something I should mention to my cancer counselor or therapist?

Yes, No, Maybe

Journal

Give yourself some grace today. ♡*Sandy*

Journal

I can do hard things through God's strength in me. Phil.4:13

He is a Life-Giving God

John 10:10

Journal

Jesus came to give me an abundant life. John 10:10

 # Journal

Date

Today I'm grateful for...

Journal

It's not over until it's over, keep pushing through. ♡Sandy

 # Journal

5-Minute Journal Prompt

2 Timothy 1:7 says that God does not give us fear.

How can we use this scripture to fight fear during this

cancer journey?

Journal

_God is planting something beautiful for you at this time. I'm still
discovering treasured blessings from my journey. ♡Sandy_

 # Journal

Today I'm grateful for...

Journal

Date _____

You don't have to be anyone's hero today. ♡Sandy

Mental Health Check-in

How I'm feeling today

Date _____

Having cancer changes our lives. What are some
changes we wish didn't happen?

_____

_____

_____

_____

_____

List some blessings that would've never happened if not
for cancer.

_____

_____

_____

_____

_____

_____

*He lovingly
wipes tears
from our eyes.
Rev. 21:4*

Is this something I should

mention to my cancer

counselor or therapist?

Yes, No, Maybe

Journal

Today I'm grateful for...

✒ Journal

_It's never one person's job to carry the world's weight. It's
especially not your job while you are trying to heal._ ♡Sandy

Journal

Rest, recover, and get back up again. ♡*Sandy*

 # Journal

Date

Today I'm grateful for...

Journal

Date

God will finish the good work he has started in me. Phi.1:6

 # Journal

5-Minute Journal Prompt

Before cancer, the sentence, "You look good," was a
compliment. Many cancer patients find that annoying
and even offensive. Why do you think that is?

Journal

Sometimes a nap can work wonders; take as needed.♡ _Sandy_

 # Journal

Date

Today I'm grateful for...

Mental Health Check-in

How I'm feeling today

Date

The words, "Remission, no evidence of disease, we have it under control, or there's nothing more we can do," put an abrupt stop to the whirlwind of cancer treatment. In what ways has the stopping of treatment impacted you physically, emotionally, and mentally?

His love lasts forever.
Jer. 31:3

Is this something I should mention to my cancer counselor or therapist?

Yes, No, Maybe

✒ Journal

God hears me when. I cry out to Him. Psalm 145:18

Journal

Date

God is my helper. Ps. 121:1-2

 # Journal

Today I'm grateful for...

Journal

As I wait on God, He gives me supernatural strength and endurance. Isaiah 40:31

Journal

God led you through the first part of this journey, and he will guide you through the rest. God will never abandon you. ♡_Sandy_

Journal

Date

"For the mountains may depart and the hills be removed, but my
steadfast love shall not depart from you." Isiaah 54:10

 **Journal**

Date

Today I'm grateful for...

My Blessing List

This is a place to list the blessings and answered prayers you've noticed throughout the journey.

Always remember Jesus' loving words to his disciples and us, "I am with you always." Matthew 28:20

If this journal was a blessing to you, help get it into the hands of more cancer patients. You can:
- Leave a review on Amazon.
- Get one for a cancer patient, or donate one to a local cancer charity for a giveaway.
- Mention it on social media, and tag me @SandyRyanPopp on Instagram, Twitter, Facebook, Pinterest, and LinkedIn.
- Use the hashtags #TheCancerJournal #ForWomen
- Visit me at www.sandyryanpopp.com for special announcements and upcoming cancer content.

Made in the USA
Las Vegas, NV
18 November 2022

59726322R00083